In Hausa culture,
the storyteller often begins,

"Ga ta nan ga ta nanku!"

"I am about to begin!"

And the children respond,

"Tazo Mujita!"

"We are all ears!"

First Printing in Ghana, 2016
Sub-Saharan Publishers
PO Box 358
Legon-Accra

ISBN: 978-1-59298-665-1
LCCN: 2017915336
Printed in the United States of America
Second Edition: 2018
22 21 20 19 18   5 4 3 2 1

Dedicated to Scheich Abubakar Hassan, the former Regional Chief Imam of the Central Region, who established the Hassaniyya Quranic School in 1969.

This book is part of a larger educational program called *The Zongo Story Project* led by Emily Williamson and John Schaidler.

For more information see:
www.zongostoryproject.com

The story and illustrations of this book grew out of a series of educational workshops directed by Emily Williamson between 2012 and 2014 with students of the Hassaniyya Quranic School in Cape Coast, Ghana. These workshops were part of the larger initiative called the *Zongo Water Project* whose mission is to use water as a way to improve the quality of life for the Zongo Community in Cape Coast, Ghana.

Thank you to the MIT Public Service Center, the University of Virginia School of Architecture, Boston University African Studies Center, Ghana Heritage Conservation Trust, Robin Dripps, Gina Haney, and my colleagues, friends, and family for making this work possible. Thank you to John Schaidler for his thoughtful editing and exceptional advice over the last year. Thank you to Mallam Mustapha Hashim Kurfi for his support and extensive help with translation. Thank you to the members of the Zongo community for their continued support, trust, and friendship. In particular, thank you to Mallam Hammadu Abubakar Hassan, Muhammad Awal Marwan, Yusuf Marwan, and the students of the Hassaniyya Quranic School for their unwavering dedication, guidance, and support throughout this project. Lastly, thank you to David Fenchel, to whom I am eternally grateful.

Beaver's Pond Press, Inc.
7108 Ohms Lane
Edina, MN 55439-2129
(952) 829-8818
www.BeaversPondPress.com

To order, visit www.ItascaBooks.com or call 1-800-901-3480 ext. 118. Reseller discounts available.

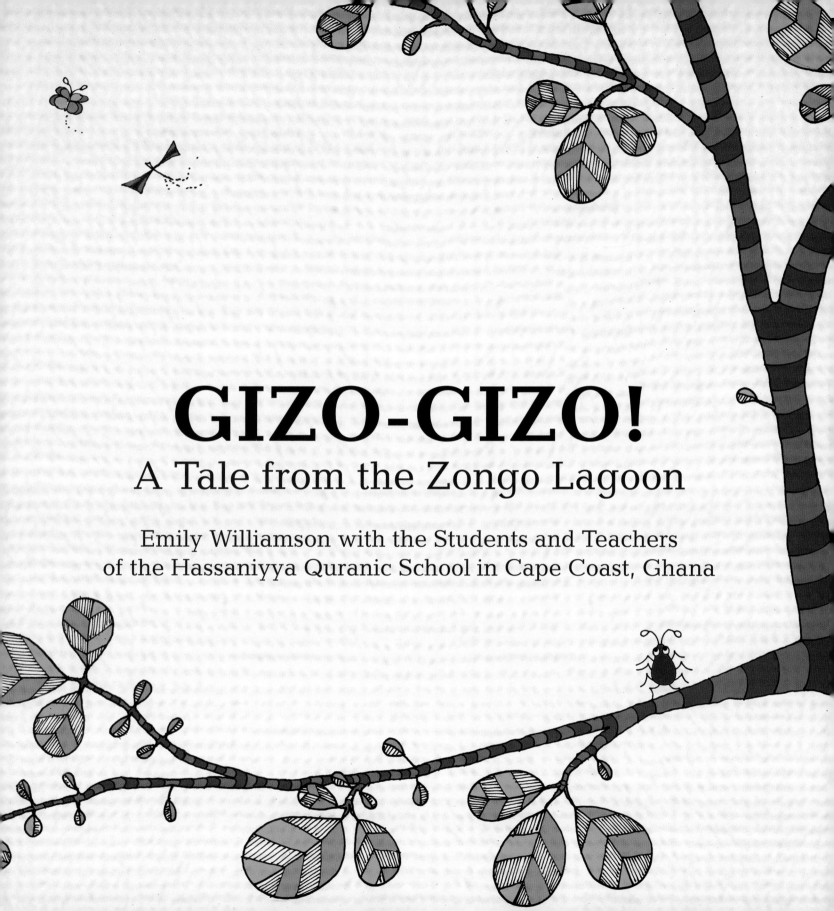

GIZO-GIZO!
A Tale from the Zongo Lagoon

Emily Williamson with the Students and Teachers
of the Hassaniyya Quranic School in Cape Coast, Ghana

Not so very long ago,
many animals lived
in the *Zongo* Lagoon.

Fish basked in the clear, clean waters.
Frogs sang in the tall green grasses.
Lizards scurried up and down
the trunks of leafy *Moringa* trees.

And down by the watery edge,
of the peaceful lagoon
that flowed into the sea,
lived three best friends . . .

Crab, Tortoise, and Spider.

A fisherman by trade,
Crab was generous and hardworking.

He spent most of his time
at the bottom of the lagoon with his family
or hauling fish into his canoe.

Tortoise was wise and patient.
Animals came to him for advice
and to buy the medicines
he made from healing roots and leaves.

HERBAL CLINIC

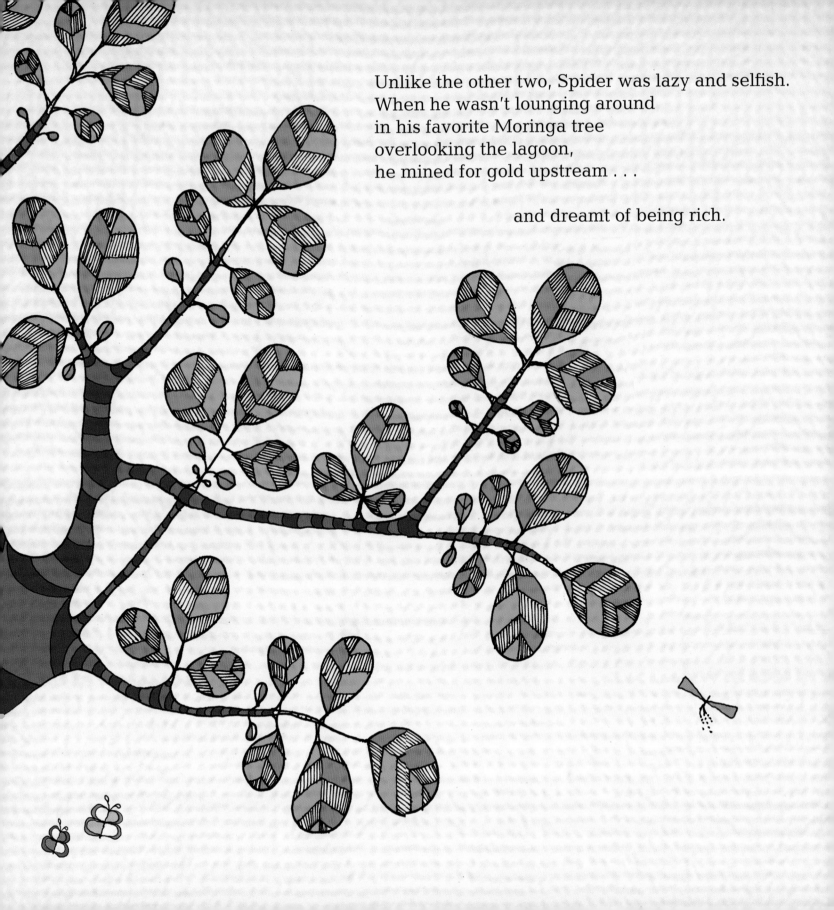

Unlike the other two, Spider was lazy and selfish.
When he wasn't lounging around
in his favorite Moringa tree
overlooking the lagoon,
he mined for gold upstream . . .

and dreamt of being rich.

Despite their differences,
Crab, Tortoise, and Spider
ate dinner together
every day at high tide.

Crab caught the fish.
Tortoise blessed the *kenkey*.

And Spider ate greedily.

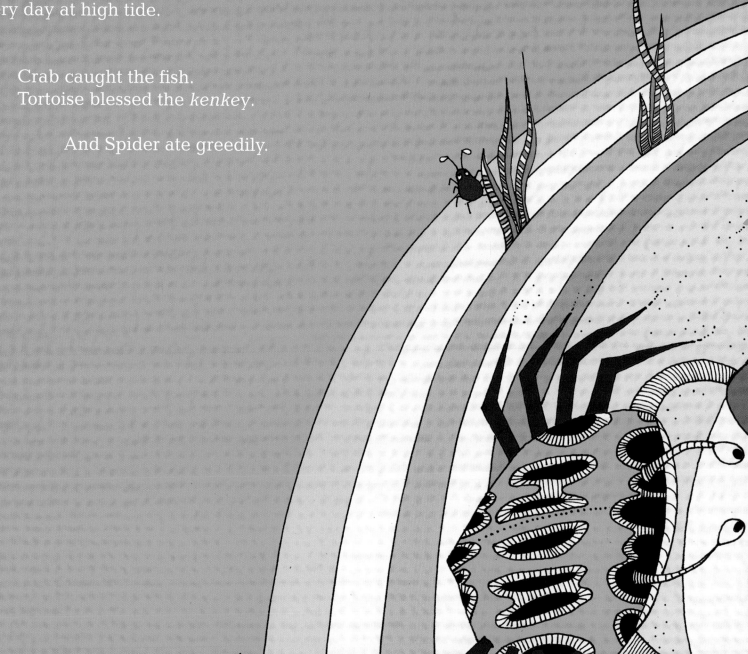

One day, after dinner,
instead of throwing his rubbish in the dustbin,
Spider tossed his kenkey leaves and plantain
peels right into the lagoon.

"*Aboki!*" Crab pleaded,
using the Hausa name for friend,
"you must respect the lagoon.
It belongs to all of us."

"Bah!" Spider bawked.
"A little rubbish is no big deal.
I own a mining business.
Someday, when I am rich, I will buy this place.
I can do whatever I want!"

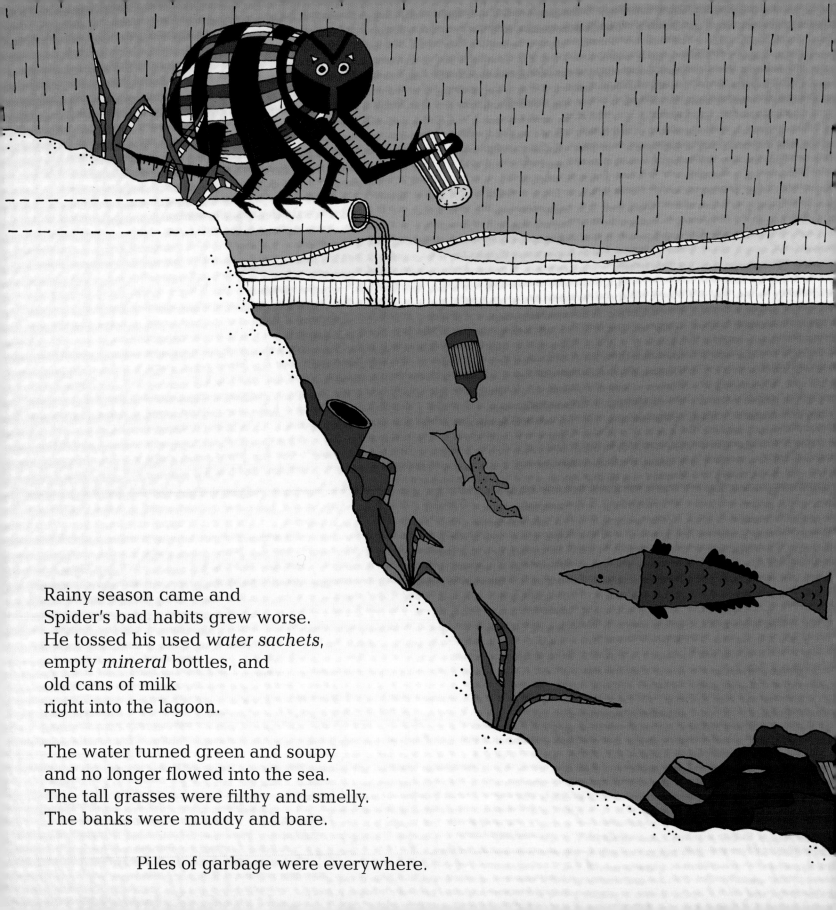

Rainy season came and
Spider's bad habits grew worse.
He tossed his used *water sachets*,
empty *mineral* bottles, and
old cans of milk
right into the lagoon.

The water turned green and soupy
and no longer flowed into the sea.
The tall grasses were filthy and smelly.
The banks were muddy and bare.

Piles of garbage were everywhere.

"Gizo-Gizo!" Crab begged,
"You must respect the lagoon.
It belongs to all of us."

"Ha!" Spider bragged.
"My mining business is booming.
A little rubbish is no big deal. Someday,
when I am rich, I will buy this place.

I can do whatever I want!"

Dry season came
and Spider's habits grew even worse.
His huge new factory polluted the lagoon
with chemicals, oil, and waste.

The animals got sick.

Fish groaned with upset stomachs.
Frogs winced from sore throats.
Lizards moaned from aching legs.

They all went to Tortoise and asked
for healing roots and leaves.

There was very little left.

Tortoise boiled the last of the *Bozobo* flowers to settle the fishes' upset stomachs.

He pounded the last of the Moringa leaves to relieve the lizards' aching legs.

He mixed the last of his salt with clean water to soothe the frogs' sore throats.

Crab shook his head sadly and said,
"This has gone on too long.
We must talk some sense into Spider's head."

DEAR GIZO GIZO,
  YOU ARE INVITED
FOR FRIED FISH AND
KENKEY ON SATURDAY
AT HIGH TIDE.
        -CRAB AND TORTOISE

GIZO GIZO GOLD MINING INC.

PO BOX 193

ZONGO LAGOON-NORTH

GHANA, WEST AFRICA

The next day,
Crab and Tortoise invited Spider to dinner—
his favorite meal of fried fish and kenkey.

Spider sat down at the table and
ate greedily, without so much as a glance
at his friends, who didn't eat one bite.

Little did Spider know
that Crab had caught the fish
from the polluted Zongo Lagoon
and that the kenkey was rotten.

Soon, Spider grew very ill.

His legs ached so badly,
he couldn't climb down
from his Moringa tree.
He tried to call to Tortoise for help,
but his throat was too sore.
He moaned and groaned from his upset stomach.

"Oh, what did I do?"

Spider cried. "I have ruined our lagoon!"

Crab and Tortoise smiled.
Perhaps Spider had learned his lesson.

"Gizo-Gizo," said Crab,

"there is only one thing to do.
You must clean up the lagoon
and never dump rubbish in it."

Tortoise nodded wisely and added,
"You must respect the lagoon.
It belongs to all of us."

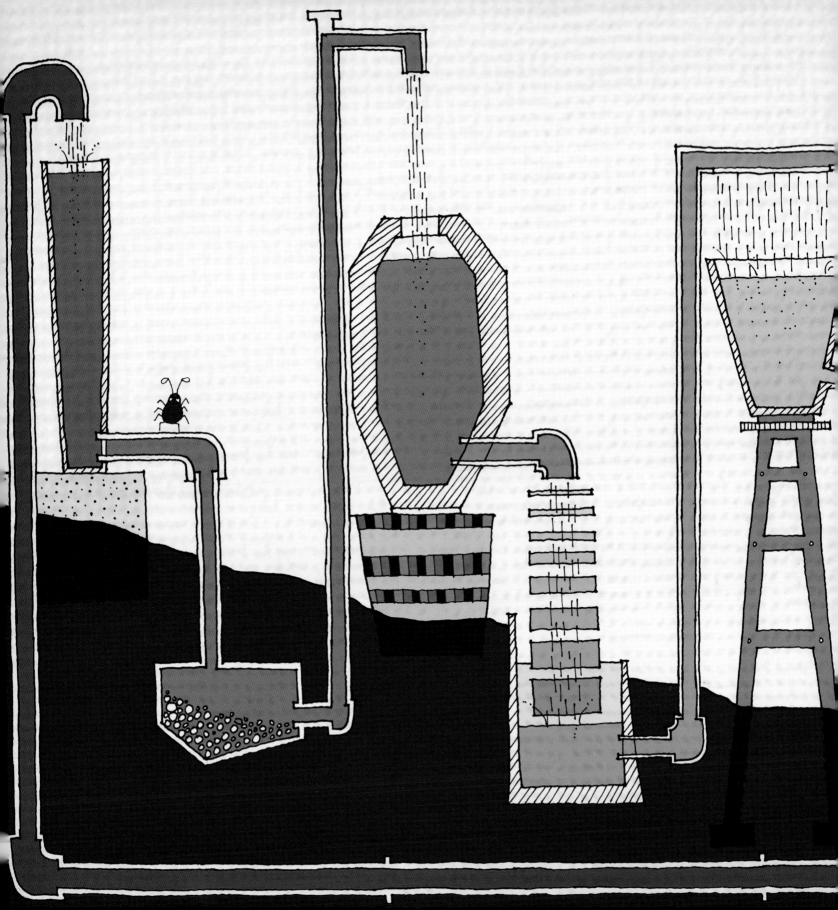

When Spider finally felt better,
he set to work
busily cleaning the lagoon.

He turned his mining business
into a place that cleaned water.

He collected rubbish from the
high grasses and removed the piles of
garbage from the bases
of the Moringa trees.

After many, many days of hard work,
Fish basked in the clear, clean waters.
Frogs sang in the tall green grasses.
Lizards scurried up and down
the trunks of leafy Moringa trees . . .

Life was peaceful once again
in the Zongo Lagoon.

So Crab, Tortoise, and Spider
enjoyed a dinner of fried fish and kenkey
together at high tide.
Crab caught the fish,
Tortoise blessed the meal, and
Spider made an announcement.

"I have learned my lesson," said Spider to his old friends.
"As my great, great grandfather used to say . . .

'The lagoon's water is sacred. It belongs to no one
and everyone at the same time.
It takes only one day to destroy it,
and many, many days to restore it.'
We must keep it clean,
every single day."

Kurunkus!

Zongo Story Project

Emily Williamson and John Schaidler
with the Zongo Community and Ghana Heritage Conservation Trust

One of the biggest challenges to children's literacy and library programs throughout many African countries is the persistent lack of access to books. Even where books are found, they tend to be secondhand copies or obscure remaindered titles from the U.S. and U.K. Ironically, it's far more common to find dog-eared Western classics on even the sparsest shelves in the most remote villages than it is to see books written and published on the African continent.

This is the crucial context in which the Zongo Story Project and the picture book *Gizo-Gizo!* were born.

Toni Morrison famously said, "If there's a book that you want to read, but it hasn't been written yet, then you must write it." The book you hold in your hands came into the world because a group of highly imaginative, eager young students from Cape Coast, Ghana—without access to books that were specifically written for them—had a powerful story to tell.

After having worked, studied, and traveled in Ghana for many years, Emily Williamson found herself in the Cape Coast zongo, working on a sanitation project. As she had done in the past, Emily also began to write and illustrate original stories with kids from the neighborhood when their work for the day was finished.

One day, a young boy raised his hand and shyly explained that a few months prior a flood of dirty water from mining companies to the north had suddenly burst forth and polluted the rivers and lakes downstream. For almost a month, the entire community was without access to clean water, the result of a negligent few. Other students chimed in with more details and personal stories about the struggles their families faced during this difficult time. Little by little, draft by draft, after many months and years, that story became this book.

As was the plan from the start, however, publication is not the end goal. Importantly, the Zongo Story Project (as the workshop is now known) centers on *process* not *product*. Accordingly, the book *Gizo-Gizo!* was used as a *mentor text* with students in Nima, Accra, in the summer of 2018 in a weeklong storybook workshop.

This is the heart and *essence* of the Full Circle publishing model. Guided by a core group of mentors, students write the book that they want to see in the world—a book that speaks to them and reflects their daily lives. Next, that book becomes a model for other student-creators who write and illustrate their own stories, too. Out and out it spirals, each community and each student spinning their own tales, in conversation with the rest, creating a whole new collection of culturally relevant classics created by and for young readers who boldly rise to the challenge set forth by Morrison.

For more information regarding the project and ways to become engaged, please visit our website at: www.zongostoryproject.com.

Na Gode! (Thank you in Hausa)

Glossary of Terms

Aboki
The Hausa word for friend.

Bozobo
A flowering plant grown in West Africa
and known for its medicinal properties.

Hausa
A language spoken in many parts of West Africa including Nigeria, Niger, and parts of Ghana.

Ghana
A country in West Africa.

Gizo-Gizo
The Hausa word for spider.

Kenkey
A popular Ghanaian dish of fermented maize wrapped in banana leaves or corn husks and steamed.

Minerals
Bubbly drinks such as soda or seltzer.

Moringa
A tree grown in Ghana and known for its medicinal properties.

Water Sachet
Small plastic bags of drinking water.

Zongo
A network of Islamic communities in Ghana.